LOVE IS

BY MARTHA EVERDS

DESIGNED AND ILLUSTRATED BY PAUL BACON

DOUBLEDAY & COMPANY, INC.   GARDEN CITY   NEW YORK

Library of Congress Catalog Card Number 78-92866
Copyright © 1969 by Martha Everds
All Rights Reserved
Printed in The United States of America
First Edition

Love is SPECIAL

LIKE A RAINBOW

and
the
first
snowfall

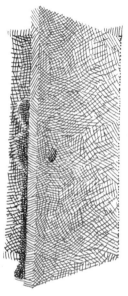

and surprises

Love is WARM

Like Summer Sand

AND THREE SOFT BLANKETS

and coming home.

Love is HAPPY

Like a ride on a roller coaster

AND

THE

PURR

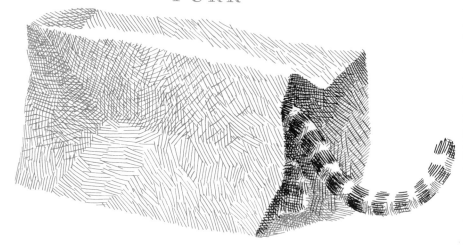

OF

A

KITTEN

AND PRETENDING.

Love is GENTLE

Like a ladybug

and soft rainfall.

and good dreams.

Love is STRONG

LIKE A GREAT TREE

AND AN ANCHOR

AND TELLING  THE TRUTH.

Love is DEPENDABLE

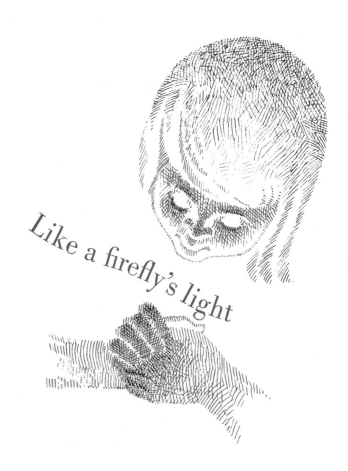

Like a firefly's light

and a heartbeat

AND   SPRINGTIME.

Love is BEAUTIFUL

Like Christmas

AND THE MOON

AND HAVING FRIENDS.

Love is BIG

LIKE THE SKY

and high, high mountains

and the word "forever"

Do you love someone?

I do.

I
love
you!